Mother God & Our Creation

Before time begins all things could be...

She begins to dream more than dreams...

by Pamela Ramsden

Illustrated by Emma Packer

Mother God & Our Creation

by *Pamela Ramsden*
Illustrated by Emma Packer

ISBN 0-9543080-0-X

Design & image manipulation by Hart Graphic Design.
Scanning & reproduction by Nutwood Associates.
Printed and bound in Hong Kong.

ACKNOWLEDGEMENTS

*This book is dedicated to my son Ben
to whom I first told the story and who has been
a constant source of support and advice.*

WITH GRATEFUL THANKS

*To all my friends, family and colleagues
who have at various times shared the journey
of this book with me – particularly:*

*Androulla, Emma, Mick, Scott, Jenny, Billie, George, Sally,
Lynn, Patricia, Anita, Ellen, Kerry, Jeni, Ray, Wendy,
Maurice and David.*

IN MEMORY OF

Vic, my brother who died before I could share these ideas with him.

*P*eople need to know how the universe and their world were created, where they come from, and why they are here.

I was brought up with two opposing explanations: one religious the other scientific. I was convinced by the rationality of science but longed for something more - something that would give a deeper meaning to life. I wanted the two ideas to be part of one story.

I continued to search for answers until much later when I learned that many ancient peoples believed in a mother goddess of the earth. Some, like the Aborigines from Australia, my birthplace, have said that the great mother created the universe. I opened myself to the idea that a cosmic mother gave birth to the universe in harmony with the laws of nature.

We can never know the answers to the mysteries of creation, but the way we think about them and the stories we tell about them affect the way we live our lives .....

DREAMS

Before tim

in shimmering c

She dreams so many...

timeless years

*B*efore time begins…
There is a mother god,
and she is all there is.

Forever she flies,
in shimmering clouds
of light,
and she is all there is.

Forever she flies,
blissfully,
in timeless oceans of light
where nothing is but her,
but where
all things might be.
Yes all things might be.

DREAMS

She begins to dream
of what might be.
She dreams so many dreams,
out of her they spill
and drift away free.

Softly
they come and go
like long shadows,
and with endless slow mist
they enfold her
till she is dreams,
all dreams.

"*We love this life,*"
yawn the dreams.
"We love how we
float and swirl,
in endless mists of what might be."

"Yes," the mother says.
"But I wish I could go
where there is more to life
than dreams.
If only I knew how;
I would be more than dreams."

she swallows up

they blast out in a searing blast

CHAPTER 2

EXPLOSION

silence, black,

and thick....

Where are my dreams?

*S*o with one huge gulp
she swallows up her dreams
and pushes them down,
way down inside of her.

"Let us go! You know we were born
to be free!" they shout.

"I know.
But I told you, I want to go
where there is more to life than you."

"I need to think
so be quiet and still
there inside me."

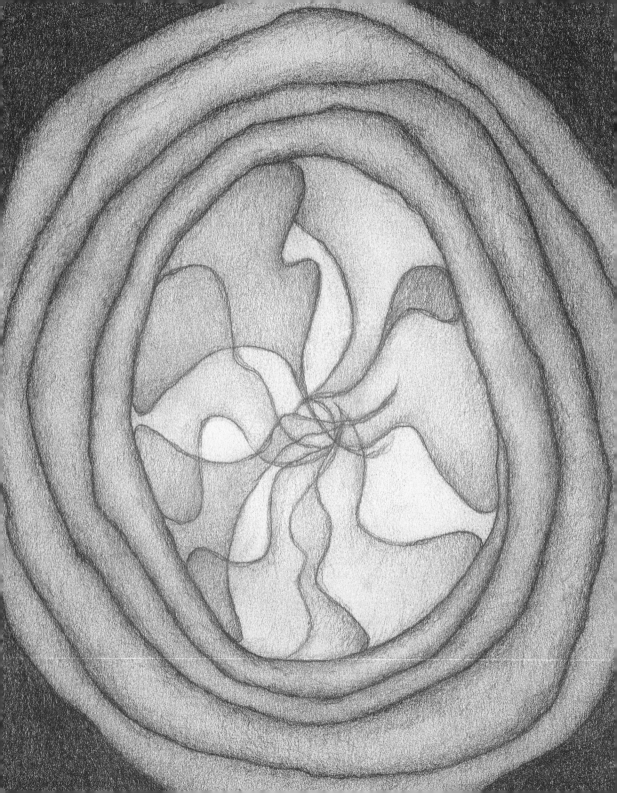

"No! Let us out!" they shout.
They struggle
and fight to get free.

The more her dreams fight
the more she presses them in
to imprison them there.

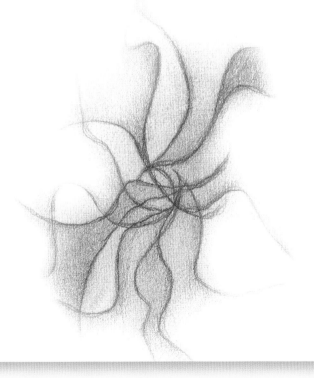

The more she presses
the more they fight.
Until she is so small and tight
and their seething force so great,
out of her they burst
in a searing blast
that seems
to go on and on.

Then there is silence.
Silence: black
and thick and still.
Nothing stirs at all.
The silence is complete.

"What is this?" she whispers.
"Where are my dreams?"

"*Why this dark silence?*
What have I done?
What is left of me now?
Why can't I see?"

"*But even if I were able to see,*
how could I bear
to see what now I must be?"

"*How stupid to dream*
of things that might be."

"*Fool to set out*
on this ill fated quest."

"*But no matter —*
I have to see
what has happened to me."

CHAPTER 3

MAGIC SPARKLES

At once in every bit of her
a curious tingling comes.

"Oooh! I feel again and it feels so good!
What can it be?"

Inside of her, and all around,
a vision of tiny winking sparks
dances in rainbow coloured patterns
like arrows, falling
through catherine wheels, bursting
into spirals of firework flowers.

"Heavenly vision what are you?"
she says aloud.
No answer comes.
"WHAT ARE YOU?"
louder she says again.

"Don't you know?
What's the matter with you?
We're a miracle of course!"
the sparks reply.

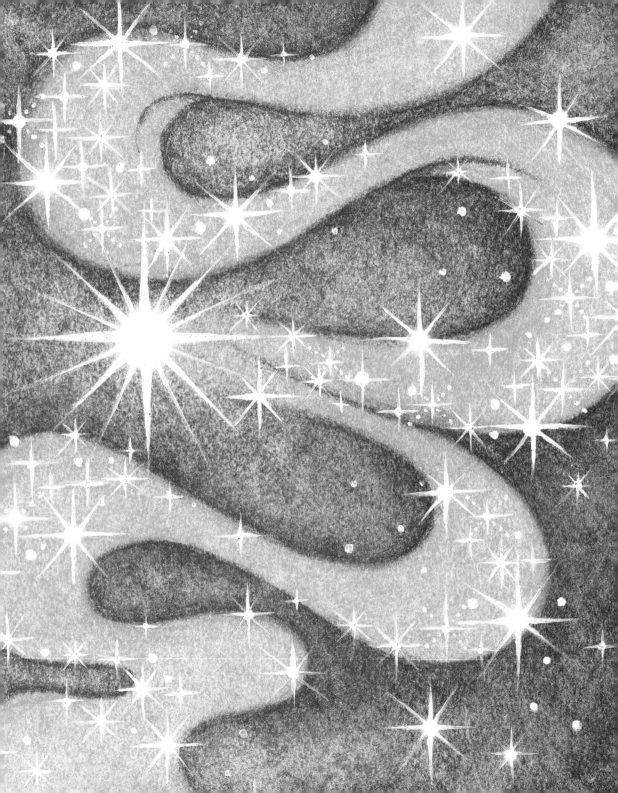

"Magic sparks, you are me
and you are not,"
she muses.
"You're all of me and part of me
yet there you are, out there
talking at me."

"Yes, Yes!" say the sparks.
"But now! Guess what!
Make haste and say the word
and you can be anything you'd like to be."

"Glory be!" she exclaims.

"Now I will be what I dreamed I might be.
Now there will be more than dreams.
Now I will be many things."

"Alright then! Let's begin!"
Words tumbling out,
she tells of all her dreams,
and the sparkles begin
to shimmer and spin.

A million magic things pop up -
now here, then there
and gone as soon as made.

There are crimson trees with purple fruit,
fairies, elves and jesters playing tricks,
mountains of jewels, feasts of sweets,
and castles like sugar in the sun.

"Fantastic!" she exclaims
as each appears,
then vanishes with another in its place,
another, and another, and still more...

"Stop!" she cries.
"They come and go too fast!
I want time to savour these.
I want to touch and taste and smell.
What is the point if none of these things last!"

"So what!" shout the sparks.
"Are you blind! Can't you see!
This is all for you.
Instant delight is yours!"

FIRE DANCE

*"No! I want to
touch and taste and smell.
I want things that last!"*

*She stamps her feet!
She claps her hands!
Flames spring
from her fingertips!*

*Red hot ash
spews from her mouth
and rains down in great mounds
all around.*

*On the smouldering mountains of ash,
she dances.*

*"I will make things that last!"
she cries.*

"Time will begin!"

Red hot ash spews from her mouth and rains down in great mounds all around.

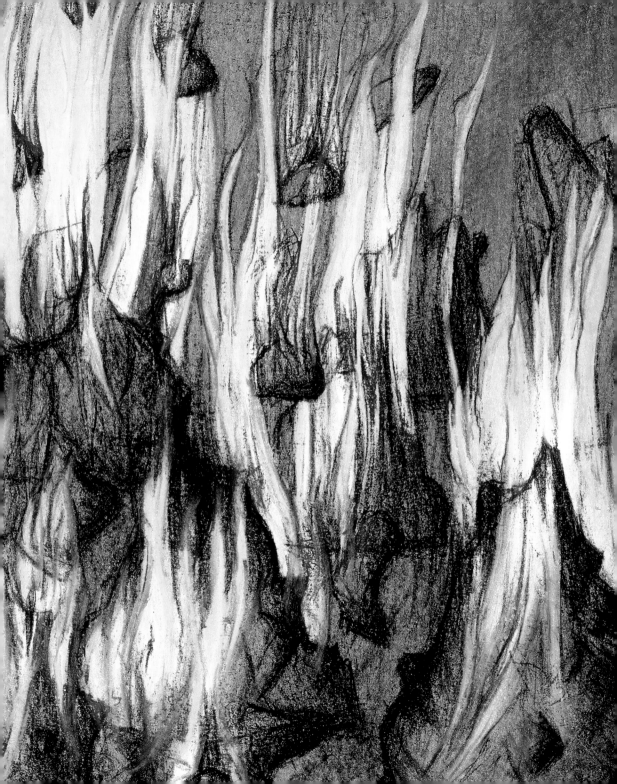

FIRE DANCE

*M*onstrous tongues of flame spring up.
They hiss and sigh.
They tower above her on every side.
Higher they climb and higher still,
closer and closer they come.
They crack and hiss and she is terrified.

She hurls thunderbolts to drive them off.
But wherever a thunderbolt strikes,
ten more rear up and jeer at her.

"Stand away from me!
You're nothing but demons!" she screams.
"I'll strike you down!
I'll fight you till the end of time!"

"Give in. You'll never win.
There's no escape," they sneer
as they close in upon her.

They trap her in their hellish furnace,
rip her apart with deadly explosions,
eat her up in their raging fire.

"What do you think of us now?"
they crow.
"We are victorious
and you are ours!"

"Yes, I know who you are,"
she groans.
"And I know what I have done."

"When first I saw you
I became afraid.
But now I know
that you and I are one.
Oh yes its true!
You are a part of me."

"Of my most magnificent self,
you are the force.
If I seek to destroy you,
who are myself,
it is myself that is devoured."

CHAPTER 5

STARS

blaze with

she sits upon a throne of fire

in a dance of majesty

...can be more

At once there is a mighty sound,
like trumpets triumphant.
Wide open spring her eyes.
They blaze with amber light.

Around her throat
curl tongues
of apricot coloured flame.
They curve above her head,
a crown of gold.

White hot is her skin.
Her crimson skirts
are billowing
swirls of flame,
and she sits
upon a throne of fire.

She is a star,
surrounded by stars,
and the stars are singing
their hearts out!

With each song of praise,
they wheel
in a dance of majesty.

The mother looks at her stars
and she is amazed.
"Good heavens," she swoons.
"Look what I have become."

*"Stars, you are me and you are not.
You're all of me and part of me
and you're separate from me."*

*"It's true! Its true!"
the stars exult.
"I know! I know!" she agrees.
"And there is still more," she says.
"I'm sure I can be more."*

*"More!" The stars exclaim.
"Ridiculous!
How could there be more than us?"*

*"You'll see," she says.
"You'll see."*

CHAPTER 6

PLANETS AND MOONS

*O*ff she zooms
through the stars' bright
halos of stardust.

Handfuls of stardust she grabs.
She scoops up
whole armfuls of stardust.
She holds them.
She rocks them.
She lets them drop,
then on she speeds for more.

Behind her
the bundles of stardust
roll over and over
around each star.

Like shining snowballs they grow,
larger and larger, until
the handfuls and armfuls
of stardust are gone.

Instead there are
planets and moons,
and around the planets,
the moons revolve.

The mother flies
from star to star.
She gathers and drops,
gathers and drops
and gathers again,
never looking back.

At last, she pauses.
She looks back and sees
the strings of planets and moons
she's left behind.
With satisfaction she smiles
and shyly they smile back at her.

"Hello," the mother says.
"How pretty you are.
And will you sing with us?"
The moons and planets glow.
Softly they begin to sing.

And so
for millions and millions of years,
mother god and her stars
and planets and moons,
sing songs of the universe.

CHAPTER 7

UNIVERSE

Every song becomes a new dance,
until there are
at least one hundred million dances,
and in each dance
at least one hundred million stars.

In great clusters wheel the stars,
slowly around each other
each one a galaxy.

There it is
laid out before her,
a glorious universe of stars, planets and moons.
In wondrous shapes
they revolve and circle and turn.

As if with stitch after stitch
of glowing thread,
they've made arcs and spirals, discs and spheres,
into a marvellous carpet of light,
sewn all across the soft, black
velvet of the night

"*W*ow!" the mother says.
"I see all this! And I'm in awe
of the glorious thing I have become!"

"Universe, I'm all of you.
I'm all and every part.
But it's not done yet," she says.
"There is a longing in my heart."

The moons, planets, and stars
are dumbfounded by this.

"Are you deaf!" they say.

"Listen! Our harmony is divine.
That is why we sing
night and day
in praise to you and all of us,
our magnificent universe."

CHAPTER 8

RESCUE

Far, far away,
a hundred thousand galaxies away,
there is a smallish star.
"I am of no importance
in the great scheme of things,"
he sighs.
"But I am a dreamer,
and there is sunshine in my heart."

He alone of all the stars
understands what is
in the mother's heart.
"I don't know how,
and no matter how far it is,
I'll go to her," he says.

As he says these words,
two great fiery wings
sprout from his back,
and he begins to fly.

"*B*ack! Back! Go back!
You must go back!
What you're doing is a crime!"
roar the stars.
But the sunny star flies on.

Galaxy upon galaxy he leaves behind
until at last he comes to the mother god.

He gathers her up and carries her
to his galaxy, white as milk.
To his own family of planets and moons he flies,
and there he sets her down.

Around her he curves his bright wings of light.
She curls into a ball.
Wrapped around by her fiery skirts
she falls fast asleep.

Lifting his wings the sun takes flight.
"No harm will come to her while I am here," he says.
High above her he comes to rest.
Folding his great wings and holding there,
his family he guards.

CHAPTER 9

SOLAR FAMILY

The first of his planets is all contrast,
blisteringly hot on one side,
the other side icy cold.
Mysterious is the next.
Full of poisonous acid,
crushing pressure and deadly heat,
it glows most brightly of all.

The fourth is fearless and red.

Light as a balloon, the fifth is huge,
in its family sixteen moons.
Most beautiful is the next,
with delicate rings around it circling
and eighteen tiny moons.

The sixth rides almost on one side.
Each of its poles is first in light
then in darkness for many years.
Buffeted by hurricanes,
the seventh has eight moons.

...the smallest planet of them all,
and always facing it is an even tinier moon.

*T*hen last and furthest from the sun,
is the little wanderer,
the smallest planet
of them all,
and always facing it
is an even tinier moon.

The sleeping mother travels,
third from the sun,
between the brightest planet
and the fearless one.

As she sleeps,
her fiery skirts begin to cool.
She rolls in the stardust around the sun
until she is quite round,
and a perfect planet she becomes.

CHAPTER 10

PLANET EARTH

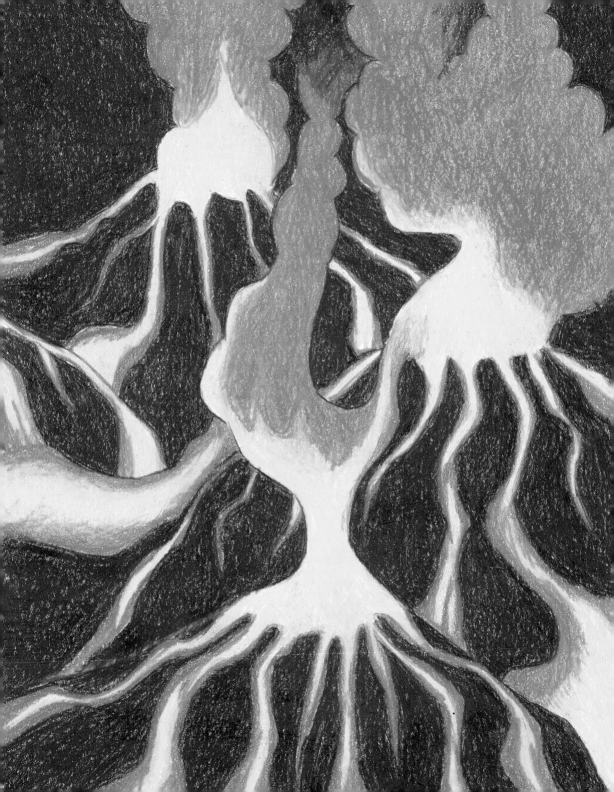

*Her new body is heavy and hot.
For it bubbles with liquid fire.
And from deep inside her
through cliffs and ledges
of solid lava
run rivers of molten rock.*

*She wakes up and looks around.
She looks and looks
as if she expects
to find something there.*

*"That longing is still in my heart," she says.
"And I can tell
that what I long for
is not here."*

She begins to cry.

She cries so much
her tears become streams.
She cries so much
the streams become rivers.
And still she cries.

The rivers become pools.
The pools become lakes.
The pools and the lakes
become rolling blue oceans.
But still she cries.

Finally to comfort her
the sun beams his fiery light down.
He warms her waters until,
the seeds of life
in her boiling depths,
in her waters begin to grow.

He warms her waters until,
the seeds of life in her boiling depths,
in her waters begin to grow

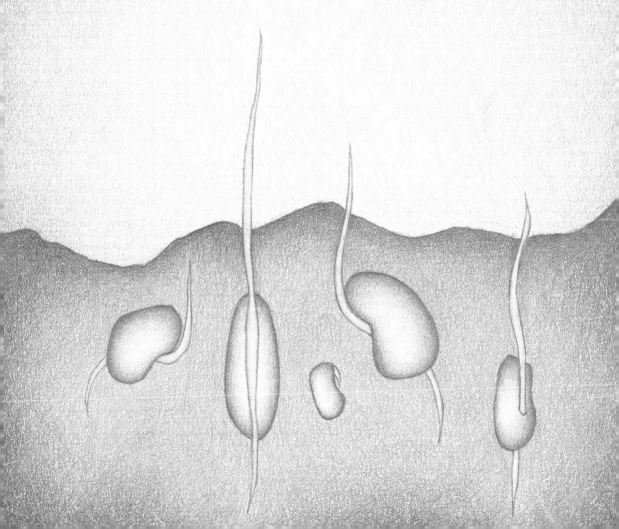

CHAPTER 11

PLANTS & FERNS
FISH & BIRDS &
OTHER ANIMALS

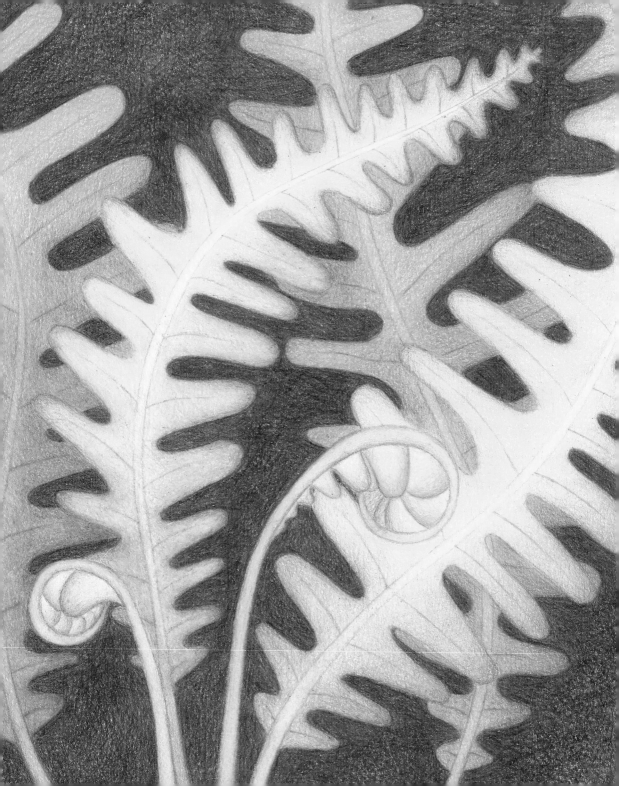

In her oceans, the fish begin to swim.
On her land grow ferns and plants.
Birds begin to fly in her air
and on her earth the animals roam.

The mother looks at the plants and ferns,
the fish, the birds and all the other animals.
"You're so beautiful," she says.

"Look at us! Look at us!"
mouth the fish.
"Look how we swim!"
"Me too! Me too!
I can swim with you!" she says.

"See how I dive and dart.
Look at me peep and start,
as from shadows
in sunlit shallows
I flee."

Through coral cathedrals
with sharks I cruise.
I brood in caverns cold.
And crawling through the murky depths,
I pierce the dark
with an octopus stare."

The birds sing "Come fly with us. Fly!"
"Yippee! I'm flying!" she replies.
"Oh how we swoop and soar.
We glide on swift air currents.
We perch on cliffs as sharp as knives
and on ponds as still as glass we float."

The animals call "Come play with us. Play!"
"Try to stop me!" she cries.
"Look at us run and lumber and lope.
We scuttle and slither and crawl.
We scamper, race, and climb
and hang upside down from trees."

"I do whatever you animals do!
Lions, with you I hunt on the plains,
with buffalo graze on the grass.
Like you mole, under the earth I burrow
and holding up my scorpion's tail,
scorched by searing winds
I sleep on desert sands."

"I am one with you my earth," she says
"and everything on you I love.
But like my ageless mountains
I must sit still and wait."

"What on earth for?" the plants and creatures say.
"It's time for fun! Aren't we all you could ever want!
And look, here we are, ready and eager
to play with you, all day!"

"Oh yes!" the mother replies.
"You are a dream fulfilled.
But there's such a longing still in my heart
and what I long for is not yet here."

And so she waits.

CHILDREN

CHILDREN

She waits until many,
many years have passed.

Then one day, her heart leaps up.
She sees children
who grow to be women and men.
The women and men have children too.
And they have many more.

And so through the garden of her earth,
people of many colours spread.
Some are black and some are brown,
others are yellow or white,
and some are red.
"These are my children," she says.

"Children, I know you.
You are me. You are all I ever was.
You are all I am and all I ever will be."

"You're one with me
and you're separate from me."

"Now I am complete."

CHILDREN

"Mother we know you too,"
the children reply.
"Like you we follow our bliss.
We make our own magic
and dream our own dreams."

"We see light glint on water,
glow in the sunset,
shimmer in the moon light,
and know we live in the light."

"We gaze up at the brilliant stars
embroidered on the black night sky,
and we know that glory is ours."

"We flee from volcanic explosions
and flows of molten rock.
From swollen rivers we run.
We sleep in a cave with sandy floor
and know we are born of this earth."

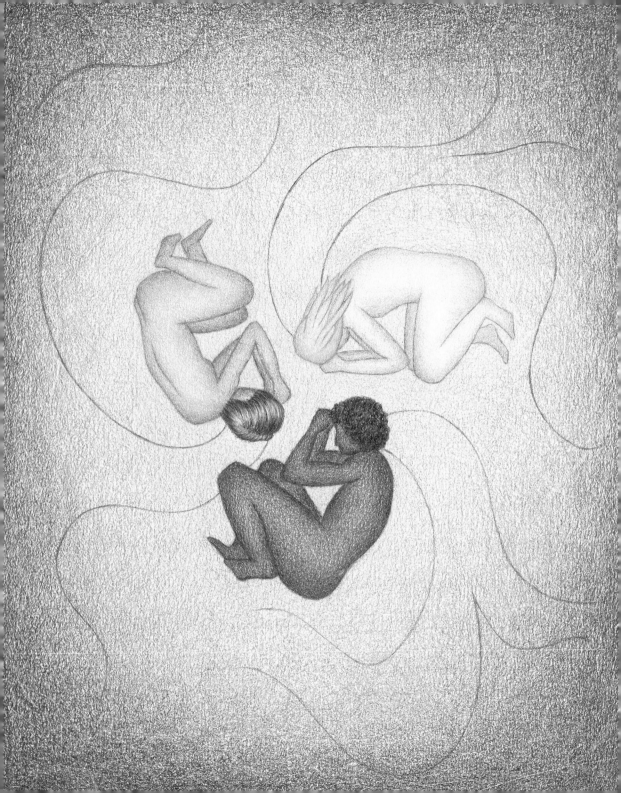

CHILDREN

"*So we will never forget who we are,
never forget from where we come
and where we will return.*"

"*We know you, our mother.
You come from the light,
through magic, by dreams,
by glory and fire,
with longing as strong as eternity
to give birth to us here on this earth.*"

"*When the gale howls we hear your pain.
When thunder rolls and lightening strikes
we tremble at your rage.*"

"*When rain falls wet on our skin
we touch your tears.
When we lie down on the earth,
we can feel you are here with us.
We listen to the whispering breeze
and hear you say to us,*"

"*I am always here.*"

CHAPTER 13

BIG HUG

" *Yes,*" *the mother says, "for I love you,
every child born on earth."*

*"I love each one of you now,
this very second and every second
of every minute
of every day.
For I am here with you,
and always will be."*

*"I hug you
in the hills and valleys of my embrace.
I calm you
with the murmur of my streams.
In the calls of my creatures,
to you I sing."*

*"You are my dearest child,
my joy, my heart's desire.
Just like me you are made.
For you and I are the same,
made the same."*

"You are my dream come true."